What Is It Now, Beetle Bailey?

Once again the madcap inmates of the Camp Swampy menagerie valiantly strive to overcome their own ineptitude—and succeed in giving us a laugh-filled book of wacky adventures.

Meet some of the more distinguished contributors to making this America's funniest comic strip.

SOME OF THE GANG AT CAMP SWAMPY

KILLER DILLER

SGT. ORVILLE SNORKEL

ZERO

LT. SONNY FUZZ

COOKIE

PLATO

CAPT. SAM SCABBARD

GEN. AMOS. T. HALFTRACK

CHAPLAIN STANEGLASS

WHAT IS IT NOW, BEETLE BAILEY ?

by Mort Walker

BOOKS

GROSSET & DUNLAP
A NATIONAL GENERAL COMPANY
Publishers   *New York*

THAT'S THE LAST BOOK I'LL EVER LEND YOU!

WHAT'S WRONG?

OH, SARGE WAS READING MY BOOK, WATCHING TV, AND EATING A SANDWICH AT THE SAME TIME

4-14

MORT WALKER

AND HE GOT HIS HANDS MIXED UP

I LIKE THAT LITTLE COMIC STRIP. IT SORTA HITS HOME

YEAH

3-9

SOMETIMES IT REFLECTS CERTAIN ATTITUDES ABOUT THE VIETNAM WAR, WESTERN HISTORY AS RELATED TO THE RACIAL PROBLEM, AND THE WHOLE SPECTRUM OF THE HUMAN CONDITION

REALLY?

OF COURSE YOU HAVE TO READ A LITTLE **INTO** IT

MORT WALKER

10-15

OTTO, THE GENERAL SAID YOU NIPPED AT HIS LEG YESTERDAY!

YOU BETTER MAKE IT UP TO HIM IN SOME WAY OR WE'LL BOTH BE SHIPPED OUT TO YOU-KNOW-WHERE!

MORT WALKER

SNORKEL!

SMAK
SMAK
SMAK

BY GOLLY, IT FINALLY HAPPENED! I HAD A DAY WHEN NOTHING WENT WRONG!

3-19

THAT'S IT, PRIVATE.. KEEP UP THE GOOD WORK AND YOU'LL BE WHAT I AM SOME DAY.

7-4